Great Scottish Inventions & Discoveries

A Concise Guide

Compiled by
John Geddes

Illustrations
Tim Archbold

NorthernBooks
from Famedram
www.northernbooks.co.uk

EUREKA!

COUCH POTATOES everywhere are probably aware that it is John Logie Baird of Helensburgh (page 6) they have to thank for giving them a screen to watch as they sit and snack. Sir Alexander Fleming (page 15) gets the credit for seeing the life saving qualities of a plate of mould and John MacAdam of Ayr (page 24) was responsible for giving us all that black stuff that now covers the country.

But what about James Chalmers of Arbroath (page 11)? John McLauchlin who emigrated to Toronto (page 23)? and James Nasmyth of Edinburgh (page 29)?

These lesser known heroes, to name but a very few, gave us, respectively: adhesive postage stamps (1834); *Canada Dry* (1890) and the steam hammer (1839), not to mention the pile driver and the dentist's drill!

The pages of this entertaining guide list many more mad – and not so mad – inventors from North of the Border who helped change the face of the world as we know it. It all adds up to a catalogue of the most amazing achievement.

Printed in Hungary.

THE INVENTORS

ANDERSON, Adam (?–d1846). Professor of Natural Philosophy at St Andrews. Contributed original papers on the measurement of the height of mountains by the barometer.

ANDERSON, James (1739–1808) of Hermiston, nr Edinburgh. Writer on political economy and agriculture. The inventor of the *Scotch Plough*.

ANDERSON, John (1726–96) of Roseneath, nr Dunfermline. Scientist. Author of *Institutes of Physics (1786)*. Creator of the *Balloon Post*. He also invented a gun which in 1791 he presented to the French National Convention

ANDERSON, Thomas (1819–74). Scottish organic chemist remembered for his discovery of Pyridine.

ARNOTT, Neil (1788–1897) of Arbroath. Became famous as a doctor and practical scientist. Prolific writer on natural science. Invented many useful appliances.

BAIN, Alexander (1810–77) of Watten, Caithness. Invented a chemical telegraph in 1843. He was also the inventor of an electric clock (1851) and a fire alarm system.

BAIRD, John Logie (1888–1946) of Helensburgh. The inventor in 1925–26 of television, which was first shown to the public in September 1929. Baird died while working on colour and stereoscopic (three dimensional) television systems.

BALFOUR, Sir Andrew (1873–1931) of Edinburgh. Novelist and expert on tropical medicine and public health. Made several important discoveries in protozoology.

BARR, Archibald (1855–1931) of Paisley. Engineer who with William Stroud founded the firm of Barr and Stroud, scientific instrument makers and pioneers in Naval range finders.

BARTHOLOMEW, John George (1860–1920) of Edinburgh. Map engraver and publisher. Best known for his system of layer colouring in contours.

BEILBY, Sir George Thomas (1850–1924) of Edinburgh. Industrial chemist. Improved the shale oil distillation and invented a manufacturing process for synthesising alkaline cyanides. He was elected a Fellow of the Royal Society.

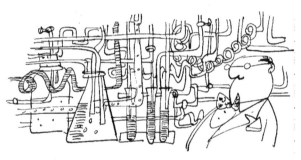

BELL, Alexander Graham (1847–1922) of Edinburgh. Went to America in 1870. Became professor of vocal physiology at Boston University in 1973. Best known for his invention of the telephone (1875–76). He also invented the photo-phone, a device for optically showing sound waves, invented a locator to detect metal objects in the human body, and produced the gramophone – an improvement on Edison's phonograph.

In 1918 he produced the HD-4 the fastest boat in the world; it reached a top speed of 70 mph (112 kph). Was a founder of the National Geographic Society.

BELL, Alexander Melville (1819–1905) of Edinburgh. Father of Alexander Graham. Teacher of elocution who invented and practised a system of invisible speech.

BELL, Sir Charles (1774–1842) of Edinburgh. Anatomist and surgeon. Discovered the functions of sensory and motor nerves. Facial paralysis, known as *Bell's palsy* is named after him.

BELL, Rev Patrick (1799–1869) of Arbroath. Invented a mechanical reaper in 1826. He did not patent his reaper and made no money out of it.

BLACK, Joseph (1728–1790) of Edinburgh. Chemist. He showed that the causticity of lime and the alkalies is due to the absence of fixed air (carbon dioxide) present in limestone and the carbonates of the alkalies. His fame rests chiefly on the theory of *Latent Heat* which he evolved.

BLAIR, Robert (?–d1828) of Murchiston, nr Edinburgh. Inventor of the fluid-filled achromatic lenses for telescopes.

BLANE, Sir Gilbert (1749–1834) of Blanfield, Ayrshire. Physician. Sailed with Rodney to the West Indies in 1779. As head of the Navy Board he was instrumental in introducing the use of citrus fruits on board ship to prevent scurvy.

BREWSTER, Sir David (1781–1868) of Jedburgh. Philosopher, physicist and inventor. Invented the kaleidoscope in 1816 and developed the stereoscope. Made important discoveries on the polarisation of light. *Brewster's Law* bears his name. He was founder of the British Association. Elected F R S.

BROWN, A B of Edinburgh. In 1870 he invented a servo-motor for hydraulic steering of ships by steam, air or oil.

BROWN, Robert (1773–1858) of Montrose. Botanist who discovered the nucleus of living cells. In 1805 he brought home about 4000 species of plants from Australia. Elected F R S in 1811.

BROWN, Thomas. Scottish engineer who in 1977 invented a computer linked 3D electric eye scanner for viewing inside the human body.

BRUCE, Sir David (1855–1931). Melbourn born Scot. Physician and naturalist. Discovered the causes of Malta fever and sleeping sickness. Elected F R S in 1884.

BUCHAN, Alexander (1829–1907) of Kinnesswood, nr Kinross. Meteorologist and pioneer of the Isobar system.

CAMERON, Charles of Glasgow. Chemist, who in 1820 invented apparatus for producing soda-water.

CAMPBELL, Angus. A Scot who in 1889 invented a spindle-type cotton-picking machine.

CHALMERS, James (1782–1853) of Arbroath. A bookseller in Dundee who invented adhesive postage stamps in 1834 – the round one penny stamp.

CLERK, Sir Dugald (1854–1932) of Glasgow. Inventor of the two-stroke motorcycle engine. He was director of the National Gas Engine Company, and director of engineering research for the Admiralty (1916).

CLERK-MAXWELL, James (1831–79) of Galloway. Physicist. First professor of Experimental Physics at Cambridge (1871). Forecast possibility of radio transmission (1865). Invented Automatic Control Systems (1868). Creator of the electro-magnetic theory of light. Described as the father of modern science he was one of Scotland's greatest sons.

CULLEN, William (1710–90) of Hamilton. Physician to whom is largely due the recognition of the important part played by the nervous system in health and disease.

CURRAN, Sir Samuel C (1912–). Educated Wishaw and Cambridge. Principal, Royal College of Science and Technology, Glasgow (1959–). Chief scientist AWRE Aldermaston (1958–59). An authority on the detection of nuclear radiation. Invented the Scintillation Detector and the modern Proportional Counter.

CURRIE, James (1756–1805) of Dumfriesshire. Physician. Chief medical work was reporting on the effects of water on Fibril diseases (1797).

DAVIDSON, Robert (1804–99) of Aberdeen. Electrical Engineer sometime described as the father of the electric locomotive. Constructed two-person electric carriage (1839) and locomotive capable of drawing 5 tons at 5 mph in 1842.

DEWAR, Sir James (1842–1923) of Kincardine-on-Forth. Professor at Cambridge. Invented the vacuum flask, discovered cordite, jointly with Sir Frederick Abel. Liquefied and froze many gases including oxygen.

DRUMMOND, Thomas (1797–1866) of Edinburgh. Inventor, administrator and statesman. The inventor of *Limelight*. He was also head of the Boundry Commission under the Reform Bill.

DUNLOP, John Boyd (1840–1921) of Dreghorn, Ayrshire. Veterinary surgeon. He invented the pneumatic tyre in 1888.

ELPHINSTONE, Sir Keith (1864–1941) of Musselburgh. Engineer who between 1893 and 1914 was connected with the invention and development of many electrical and mechanical devices. He designed the first chart recorder, and invented the speedometer for motor cars.

ELPHINSTONE, William (1431–1514) of Glasgow? Statesman and lecturer on law in Paris and Orleans. Ambassador to France under James IV (1491). Was responsible for introducing the printing press (Chapman & Millar) into Scotland.

FAIRBAIRN, Sir William (1789–1874) of Kelso. Civil and mechanical engineer and inventor. First in the utilisation of iron for shipbuilding. Devised a riveting machine. He also built bridges (nearly 1000). Elected F R S in 1850.

FAIRLIE, Robert. Scottish engineer and inventor – in 1863 – of a railway engine with pivoted driving bogies, allowing trains to negotiate tighter bends.

FERGUSON, Patrick (1744–80) of Pitfour, Aberdeenshire. Inventor of a breech-loading rifle. In 1776 he patented his rifle which was capable of firing seven shots a minute and sighted for ranges 100 to 500 yards

FLEMING, Sir Alexander (1881–1955) of Darvel, Strathclyde. Bacteriologist. Discovered Penicillin in 1928. Elected F R S in 1943. Nobel Prize for medicine in 1945.

FLEMING, Sir Sandford (1827–1915) of Kirkcaldy. Canadian engineer. Took a prominent part in railway development in upper Canada. Chief engineer, Northern Railways (1855–63). He was the originator of *Standard Time*.

FORBES, James D (1809–68) of Edinburgh. Scientist and writer. Was one of the founders of the British Association in 1831. His investigations and discoveries embraced the subject of heat, light polarisation and especially glaciers.

FORBES, Sir John (1787–1861) of Cuttlebrae, Banffshire. Physician. Was joint editor of *Cyclopaedia of Practical Medicine* (1832–35). Translated Annenbrugger and Laennec and thus advocated use of the Stethoscope in this country.

FORSYTH, Alexander John (1768–1843) of Belhelvie, Aberdeenshire. Clergyman and inventor. In 1807 patented his application of the detonating principal in firearms, which was followed in 1808 by the adaption of the percussion cap. He was pensioned by the British Government after refusing to sell his secret to Napoleon.

GED, William (1690–1749) of Edinburgh. Printer and goldsmith. Invented a process of stereotyping in 1725.

GILL, Sir David (1843–1914) of Aberdeen. Astronomer to the Cape Observatory (1897–1907). Pioneered the use of photography as a means of charting the heavens.

GORDON, Sir Robert (1647–1704) of Gordonstoun. Inventor and reputed warlock. Designed a pump for raising water.

GREGORY, David (1661–1708) of Kinairdy, Perthshire. Mathematician. In 1691 became Savilian professor of Astronomy at Oxford. He it was who first suggested an achromatic combination of lenses.

GREGORY, James (1638–75) of Drumoak, Aberdeenshire. Mathematician and astronomer. A leading contributor to the discovery of the differential and integral calculus. Invented the reflector telescope.

GREGORY, James (1753–1821) of Aberdeen. Physician who gave his name to *Gregory's Mixture*.

HALL, Sir James (1761–1832) of Dunglass. Geologist. He sought to prove the geological theories of his friend and master (Hutton) in the laboratory, and so founded experimental geology.

HARRISON, James. Of Scottish descent, invented a refrigerator at a brewery in Bendigo, Australia in 1851. He later turned to the refrigeration of meat. In 1873 he gave a public banquet of meat that had been frozen in his ice factory.

HENRY, Joseph (1797–1878), born in America of Scottish parentage. Physicist. Made important discoveries on the subject of electro-magnetic induction.

The *Henry* (of induction) is named after him. In 1840 he became the first secretary and director of the Smithsonian Institute, Washington.

HILL, David Octavius (1802–70) of Perth. Landscape and portrait painter. The first to apply photography to portraiture.

HOLDEN, Sir Isaac (1807–97) of Hurlet, Renfrewshire. Mathematician and inventor. Studied chemistry in his leisure hours. Invented the *Lucifer* match, but was anticipated by John Walker of Stockton.

Holden was an associate of Lister.

HORSBURGH, Thomas. Scottish blacksmith who devised the first steel-shafted golf club in 1894.

HUTTON, James (1726–97) of Edinburgh. Geologist. The *Huttonian* theory, emphasising the igneous origin of many rocks and depreciating the assumption of other causes than those we see still at work, was expounded before the Royal Society of Edinburgh in *A Theory of the Earth* (1785). It formed the basis of modern geology.

ISAACS, Alick (1921–67) of Glasgow. Virologist and discoverer of Interferon in 1952.

KEILLER, Mrs Keiller of Dundee. The first to produce marmalade in 1797. Her son founded the Keiller Company, and marmalade became popular throughout the world.

KELVIN of LARGS (William Thomson) 1st Baron (1824–1907). Born in Belfast of Scots descent. Physicist, mathematician, philosopher, engineer, and inventor. Discovered the second law of thermodynamics.

Inventor of telegraphic and scientific instruments etc, including the improved mariner's compass and sounding equipment.

Elected F R S in 1851. Buried in Westminster Abbey.

Lord Kelvin's improved mariner's compass

KENNEDY, John (1769-1855) of
Kirkcudbrightshire. Cotton-spinner and inventor.
Introduced several ingenious improvements in the
spinning of fine yarns, including the *Jack frame*.

KERR, John (1824–1907) of Ardrossan. Physicist
and lecturer in mathematics. In 1876 he discovered
the *magneto–optic–effect* which was named after
him. He was the author of *An Elementary Treatise on
Rational Mechanics* (1867). Elected F R S.

LAIRD, John (1805–74) of Greenock. Shipbuilder. One of the earliest constructors of iron vessels.

LAPWORTH, Arthur (1892–1941) of Galashiels. Original chemist. Remembered for his enunciation of the electronic theory of organic clinical reactions in 1920.

Appointed to the Chair of Physical and Inorganic Chemistry in 1922. Elected F R S.

LEE, James Paris (1831–1904) of Hawick. Watchmaker.

Invented the remarkably efficient bolt-action and magazine of the Lee–Metford (later Lee-Enfield) rifle about 1890.

LEISHMAN, Sir William B (1896–1926) of Glasgow. Bacteriologist. Professor of Pathology in the Army Medical College and Director-General, Army Medical Service (1923).

He discovered an effective vaccine for inoculation against typhoid, and was first to discover the parasite disease Kala-azar.

LINDSAY, James Bowman. Invented the first electric light bulb in 1835 in Dundee.

LESLIE, Sir John (1766–1832) of Largo, Fife. Mathematician, natural philosopher and inventor. His many inventions include, a differential thermometer, Hygrometer, Photometer, Atometer and Althriscope. His researches appeared in 1804 in his *Experimental Inquiry into the Nature and Properties of Heat.* In 1804 he successfully applied the absorbent powers of sulphuric acid to freeze water under the receiver of the air pump. This is the first recorded achievement of artificial congelation.

LOW, Archibald Montgomery (1886–1956), education, Skerry's College, Glasgow. Physicist and inventor. His numerous inventions include a system of radio signalling, a television system (1914), electrical rocket control (1917), a coal-fuel engine, radio torpedo control gear, the vibrometer and audimeter. Was president of the British Institute of Engineering Technology and of the Institute of Patentees.

MacADAM, John Loudon (1756–1836) of Ayr. Inventor of the *Macadamizing* system of road-making commonly known as *Tarmac*. He was appointed surveyor of Britain's roads in 1827. MacAdam refused a Knighthood.

MacARTHUR, John (1767–1834).

A Scotsman who became known as the father of New South Wales, Australia.

Introduced sheep and planted the first vineyard there in 1817.

MacEWEN, Sir William (1848-1924) of Rothesay. Surgeon. Founder of aseptic surgery and pioneer in surgery of the brain and lung, and in orthopaedic surgery.

MacKENZIE, Sir George S, (1780–1848). Mineralogist. First to obtain proof of the identity of diamond with carbon.

MacKENZIE, Sir James (1853–1925) of Stone, Perthshire. Physician. The inventor of the Polygraph to record graphically the heart's action. Elected F R S in 1915.

McLAUCHLIN, John. A Scottish chemist in Toronto. Invented the popular soft drink known as *Canada Dry* in 1890.

MacLEOD, John James Rickard (1876–1935) of Cluny, nr Dunkeld. Physiologist. Professor of Physiology at Cleveland, Ohio (1903–18), Toronto (1818–28).

Celebrated for his work on the isolation of insulin for which he won a Nobel prize. his father belonged to Wick, Caithness.

MacMILLAN, Kirkpatrick (1813–78) of Keir, Dumfriesshire. Blacksmith. Invented the first cycle to be propelled by cranks and peals (about 1840). A replica of his machine can be seen in the Science Museum, South Kensington. He was fined 5/- (the first recorded cycling fine) for knocking over a child. An unofficial dentist he also pulled teeth from both men and horses. He was known locally as *Daft Pate*.

McNAUGHT, John (1813–81) of Paisley. Engineer and inventor of the Compound Steam Engine.

MANSON, Sir Patrick (1844–1922) of Oldmeldrum. Physician who became known as the father of tropical medicine. The first, jointly with Sir Ronald Ross, to discover that parasites were transmitted by insects. He was sometimes known as *Mosquito Manson*.

MEIKLE, Andrew (1719–1811) from near Dunbar. A prolific inventor. Fantail gear (1750) and governing sails (1772) for windmills, a grain dressing machine (1768) and a drum threshing machine (1784) were but four of his inventions.

MELVILLE, Thomas (1726–53) of Glasgow. Scientist. Was the first (1752) to study the spectra of luminous gases.

MENZIES, Andrew. Scottish mining engineer. Invented a horse and man-powered coal-cutting machine in 1863.

MILLAR, Patrick (1731–1815) from near Dumfries. Inventor and projector of steam navigation.

MILLER, Maxwell of Glasgow. In 1850 invented an improved still for distilling and rectifying spirits.

MONCRIEFF, Sir Alexander (1829–1906) of Perthshire. Soldier and inventor. In 1868 he invented and developed the *Moncrieff Pit,* or *Disappearing System.* A method of mounting heavy guns in coastal batteries. The gun disappeared after firing and reappeared when required through the use of stored recoil energy.

MUNRO, Alexander (1733–1817) of Edinburgh. Anatomist. Wrote on the nervous system (1783), the physiology of fish (1785) and on the brain, eye and ear (1797). Was the first to describe the use of a stomach tube.

MORTON, Thomas (1781–1832). Scottish shipbuilder and inventor, (about 1822) of the patent slip which provided a cheap substitute for a dry-dock.

MURDOCK (originally Murdoch) William (1754–1839) of Bello Mill, Old Comnock. Miller and millwright. A prolific inventor. In 1785 he invented

a steam tricycle, gas lighting from coal (1796–1803), a steam cannon (1803), worm-driven cylinder-boring machine (1810) and a crown-saw boring machine. He also perfected underwater paint for ships.

MUIR, John (1838–1914) of Dunbar. Naturalist, explorer and inventor. He was also a conservationist who became known as the father of United States conservation. His inventions include a self-setting water-powered saw mill, various locks, hygrometers, clocks and pyrometers.

NAPIER, John (1550–1617) of Merchiston Castle, Edinburgh. Mathematician and the inventor of Logarithms (1614) and civil engineering devices.

NASMYTH, James (1808–90) of Edinburgh. Engineer and inventor of the steam hammer in 1839 and later a pile driver and a dentist's drill.

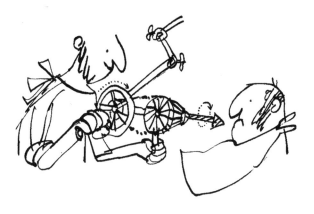

NEILSON, James Beaumont (1792–1865) of Shettleston. Engineer and inventor. In 1828 he patented his hot blast process, the technique of preheating the blast air in blast furnaces.

NICOL, William (c1768–1851). The Scottish inventor of the Nicol Prism which bears his name.

RAMSAY, Sir William (1852–1916) of Glasgow. Professor of Chemistry at Bristol (1880–87) and University College, London (1887–1912). In conjunction with Lord Rayleigh he discovered the gas Argon in 1894. Later he discovered Helium, Neon, Krypton and Xenon. He won a Nobel prize for Chemistry in 1904. Elected F R S in 1888.

RILEY, James of Glasgow. Engineer who invented nickel-steel in 1889.

ROPER, Andrew of Hawick. A farmer who in 1737 invented a winnowing machine.

ROSS, Sir Ronald (1857–1932). Born in Almora, India of Scottish parents. Physician who discovered – jointly with Patrick Manson – that malaria parasites were carried by mosquitoes and transmitted to their victims while sucking blood (1895–98).

RUSSEL, John Scott (1808–82) of Parkhead, Glasgow. Civil engineer and Naval architect. Invented the *wave system* of shipbuilding. He built the *Great Eastern* and other ships.

RUTHERFORD, Daniel (1749–1819) of Edinburgh. Physician and botanist. In 1772 published his discovery of the distinction between *noxious air* (nitrogen) and carbon dioxide. Subsequent study on the construction of natural gases was founded on his works. In 1794 he invented a maximum/minimum thermometer.

RUTHERFORD, Ernest (1871–1937). New Zealand born of Scottish descent. Physicist. Pioneer in atomic research. First to split the atom.

SHIRREFF, Patrick (1791–1876) of Haddington, East Lothian. Farmer who was a pioneer of cereal hybridising. He produced many varieties of wheat and oats.

SIMPSON, Sir James Young (1811–70) of Bathgate. Obstetrician and professor of midwifery. Discovered chloroform in 1847, having experimented on himself.

SINCLAIR, Daniel (Dane)(1852–1930) of Thrumster, Caithness. Telephone engineer and inventor of the telephone exchange. He was also the inventor of the hollow solder tube containing fluxite. In his day he was regarded as one of the leading telephone engineers in the world. He became chairman of several power distribution and telephone companies.

SINCLAIR, James, 14th Earl of Caithness (1824–81). He patented many ingenious inventions, including a loom, steam carriage and a gravitating compass.

SMITH, Adam (1723–90) of Kirkcaldy. Regarded as the father of modern economics. His book *The Wealth of Nations* was the product of the mind of the first systematic academic economist.

SMITH, James (1789–1850) of Deanston, Perthshire. Agricultural engineer and philanthropist. The inventor of *through drainage* by means of a subsoil plough (1823). He was the inventor of a rotary reaping machine in 1811.

STEVENSON, Robert (1772–1850) of Glasgow. Builder of lighthouses (including Bellrock). Invented the flashing system. Was also a consulting engineer for roads, bridges, harbours, canals and railways. He built 23 Scottish lighthouses. Robert Louis Stevenson was his grandson.

STEVENSON, Thomas (1818–87) of Edinburgh. Son of Robert. Joined with his father and brother

David in lighthouse construction and lighting methods in particular. He was the inventor of the thermometer screen, which is known by his name.

STIRLING, Rev Dr Robert (1790–1878) of Methven, Perthshire. Invented a type of gas-sealed internal combustion engine in 1817. His engine has been recently re-examined by British, Dutch and American engineers in connection with the development of a low pollution engine.

SYMINGTON, William (1763–1831) of Leadhills. Millwright and inventor. In 1787 he patented an engine for a road locomotive and in 1788 built one of the first steamboats. It had two paddle-wheels in the middle of the deck. He was also the inventor of a horizontal direct-acting engine which he patented and fitted in a tug called Charlotte Dundas in 1801–2. It was the first workable steam ship ever produced. He died in poverty in London.

TAIT, Peter Guthrie (1831–1901) of Dalkeith. Mathematician, physicist and philosopher. Professor of mathematics at Belfast (1854). Produced the first working thermo-electric diagram. Published many papers on scientific subjects.

TASSIE, James (1735–99) of Pollokshaws. Engraver and modeller. Famed for his paste and imitation gems. Was commissioned by Catherine the Great of Russia to supply her with some 15000 items of imitation gems and cameos. He invented the white enamel composition which he used for his medallion portraits.

TELFORD, Thomas (1757–1834) of Langholm. Son of a shepherd. A civil engineer who changed the face of Britain. Builder of bridges, aqueducts, canals and docks. The Menai Suspension Bridge was perhaps his greatest work (1825). Buried in Westminster Abbey.

TEMPLETON, James (1802–?) Scottish carpet manufacturer. Devised modification of Chenille velvet technique and applied it to the pile carpets and furnishings. Founded his Glasgow factory in 1839. Received several Royal Commissions from Queen Victoria for carpet. In 1850 licensed other carpet manufacturers to use his invention.

TENNANT, Charles (1768–1838) of Ochiltree, Ayrshire. Pioneer chemical industrialist. Developed and manufactured a bleaching powder.

THOMSON, James (1822–92). Scottish engineer born in Belfast. Brother of Lord Kelvin. He was an authority on hydraulics. Invented a turbine, discovered the effect of pressure upon the freezing-point of water and wrote papers on elastic fatigue, undercurrents and trade winds.

THOMSON, Sir Joseph John (1856–1940). Born near Manchester, son of a Scottish antiquarian bookseller. Physicist and discoverer of the Electron in 1897. Nobel prize winner for physics in 1906.

THOMSON, Robert William (1822–73) of Stonehaven. Civil engineer, inventor and expert on blasting. Designed and improved machine for making sugar in Java, invented a mobile crane, and in 1845, the first pneumatic tyre, but it was considered a curiosity and not developed, India rubber being very expensive at that time. He was also the inventor of a dry-dock and a fountain pen.

THOMSON, Thomas (1773–1852) of Crieff. Chemist. When making investigations in brewing and distillation, he invented the instrument known as *Allan's saccharometer*.

THOMSON, Thomas (1817–78) of Glasgow. Surgeon and naturalist. Discovered pectic acid in carrots.

TODD, Alexander R, 1st Baron Trumpington (1908–?) of Glasgow. Chemist and scientist, sometimes described as the most eminent Scottish scientist since Lord Kelvin. Has been honoured by the Russians for outstanding achievements in organic chemistry. Nobel Prize winner for research on vitamins B and E. Elected F R S in 1942.

URE, Andrew (1778–1851) of Glasgow. Chemist. Sometime Professor of Chemistry and Natural Philosophy at Anderson's College, and Analytical Chemist the the Bd of Customs, India (1834). He was the inventor of the Alkalimeter (1816) and a Bimetal Thermostat in 1830. Produced a *Dictionary of Chemistry* (1812). Elected F R S in 1822.

WALLACE, Alfred Russel (1823–1913). Born in Usk of Scottish descent. Architect, land surveyor and naturalist. Independently formulated the theory of natural selection before Darwin.

WATERSTON, John James (1811–83) of Edinburgh. Developed early kinetic theory of gases.

WATSON-WATT, Sir Robert Alexander (1892–1973) of Brechin. Physicist and inventor. Appointed Scientific Advisor to the Air Ministry in 1940. Invented and developed radar.

WATT, James (1736–1819) of Greenock. Mathematical instrument maker and prolific inventor. Developed the improved steam engine, invented the condenser (1765), sun and planet gears (1784), the governor, water gauge, parallel motion, smokeless furnace and a letter copying machine. The *watt* as a unit of electrical power is named after him.

WHYATT, Robert (1714–66) of Edinburgh. Neurologist who pioneered study of reflex action.

WILSON, Charles Thomson Rees (1869–1959) of Glencorse. Physicist. Pioneer in atomic and nuclear physics. Professor of Natural Philosophy at Cambridge (1923–34). Famous for his invention of the *Wilson Cloud Chamber,* an indispensable tool of modern physics ever since, and for which he was awarded a Nobel Prize for physics in 1927.

WILSON, Robert (1803–82) of Dunbar. Inventor of the screw propeller for ships, and in 1861 a double-acting steam hammer.

WILLIAMSON, John (1740–1803) (nicknamed *Johnnie Notions*) of Eshaness, Shetland. Weaver, blacksmith, carpenter and true pioneer in the fight against smallpox by serum inoculations. He was also a clock repairer and frequently dabbled in mechanical inventions, thus earning his nickname.

WOOD, Alexander (1817–84). Scottish physician who advocated the use of the hypodermic syringe for injections.

YOUNG, James (1811–89) of Glasgow. Scientist and founder of world's first commercial oil works (1851) after discovering a method of distilling oil from shale. Was sometime known as *Paraffin Young*. He was a great friend of David Livingstone, to whom he gave financial help, having amassed a large fortune. Elected F R S in 1873.

TERRITORIAL DISCOVERIES
By Explorers & Missionaries

BAIKIE, William Balfour (1825–64) of Kirkwall, Orkney. Surgeon, explorer, naturalist and linguist. Opened the navigation of the Niger. Constructed roads and founded a city state. Translated the Bible into several languages of Central Africa.

BRUCE, James (1730–94) of Kinnaird, Stirlingshire. Explorer in Africa. First to find the source of the Blue Nile. Discovered Tissisat Falls in 1770. His *Travels to Discover the Source of the Nile* (1790) was published in five volumes. Described as a formidable man, Bruce was 6'4" in height and strong in proportion. Had dark red hair and a very loud voice. He died as the result of tripping and falling down stairs when offering his hand to a lady.

CADELL, Francis (1822–79) of Cockenzie. Explorer in Australia. Explored the Murray River. Was murdered by his crew.

CLAPPERTON, Hugh (1788–1827) of Annan. Explorer in Africa. Died in his attempt to discover the source of the Nile.

COOK, Captain James (1728–79) born at Marton, Yorkshire, son of a Scottish (Roxburgh) farm labourer. Naval Officer, explorer and scientific navigator. Charted the east coast of Australia and named it New South Wales. He mapped much of the Southern Hemisphere and discovered the Sandwich (Hawaiian) islands where he was killed.

DOUGLAS, David (1798–1834) of Scone. Botanical traveller in North America. Discovered many new species of flora and introduced to Britain many trees and herbaceous plants, including the Douglas Fir which bears his name.

LAING, Alexander Gordon (1793–1826) of Edinburgh. Explorer. Served as naval officer in the West Indies for 7 years. Was sent to explore the Niger's source, which he found, but was murdered after leaving Timbuktu.

LANDSBOROUGH, William (1825–?) of Stevenston, Ayrshire. Explorer who with John McDouall Stuart was first to cross Australia in 1861–62.

LIVINGSTONE, David (1813–73) of Blantyre. Explorer and missionary in Africa. Discovered Zambesi river, Victoria Falls, Lakes Nyasa, Shirwa, Mweru, and Bangweulu. Buried in Westminster Abbey.

MacKAY, Alexander Morehead (1849–90) of Rhynie, Aberdeenshire. Engineer and pioneer missionary to Uganda (1878–87). Became known as *MacKay of Uganda*. Died of a fever at Usumbiro.

MacKAY, JAMES, Scottish botanist who discovered the sources of the Mississippi and Missouri rivers in 1784.

MacKENZIE, Sir Alexander (1764–1820) of Stornoway. Explorer and fur trader in N W Canada. The MacKenzie River which bears his name was discovered by him in 1789. He crossed the Rockies to the Pacific (1792–93).

MacKINNON, Quintin (?–d1892) of Argyll. Surveyor and explorer. Discovered MacKinnon's Pass in New Zealand about 1888.

PARK, Mungo (1771–1806) of Foulshiels, Selkirk. Botanist and explorer in Africa, and of the River Niger. Discovered the source of the Niger in 1796. Told of his adventures in *Travels in the Interior of Africa* (1799).

RAE, Dr John (1813–1893) of Stromness, Orkney. Explorer and Arctic traveller. Commanded an expedition (1853–54) to King William's Land. In 1854 he discovered the fate of the Franklin expedition, for which he was awarded £10,000. in 1860 he surveyed a telegraph line to America via Faroes and Iceland, and in 1864 surveyed a telegraph line from Winnipeg over the Rocky Mountains. He also mapped the north coast of Canada for the Hudson's Bay Company.

ROSS, Sir James Clark (1800–62) born in London of Wigtownshire forebears. Rear Admiral and explorer. Discovered the Ross sea which bears his name. He was also responsible, with his uncle, Sir John Ross, for the establishment of the true position of the magnetic north.

ROSS, Sir John (1777–1856) of Wigtownshire. Rear Admiral and explorer in Baffin Bay. Discovered the Boothia Peninsula in his search for the north west passage to the pole. With his nephew Sir James Clark Ross he established the true position of magnetic north. Was Consul at Stockholm (1839–46).

SELKIRK, Thomas Douglas, 5th Earl of (1771–1820). Explorer and coloniser. Settled emigrants from the Scottish Highlands in Prince Edward Island (1803) and Red River Valley, Manitoba. Became known as *Selkirk of Red River*.

SIMPSON, Sir George (1792–1860), Scottish Canadian explorer and administrator (1821–56) of Hudson Bay Company and its territory. Made an over-land journey around the world in 1828. Simpson's Falls and Cape George Simpson are named after him.

SIMPSON, Thomas (1808–40) of Dingwall. Explorer in the Canadian Arctic. Simpson Strait bears his name.

STUART, John McDouall (1815–66) of Dysart, Fife. Surveyor and explorer in Central Australia. Mount Stuart is named after him. With William Landsborough, the first men to cross Australia south to north (1861–62).

SUTHERLAND, Donald (1835–1919) of Wick, Caithness. Became known as *The Hermit of Milford Sound* in New Zealand. Discovered Sutherland Falls (one of the world's highest) which bears his name at Milford Sound. Sometime served in Italy with the forces of Garibaldi.

THOMSON, Joseph (1858–95) of Penpont, Dumfriesshire. Geologist and explorer in Tanganyika (1878–79) and Masai country (1883–84). The Thomson Gazell and Thomson Falls in Kenya are named after him. He explored Southern Morocco for the Geographic Society in 1888.